# Mental Health (Patients in the Community) Act 1995: an introductory guide

## Central Health Studies

The Central Health Studies (CHS) series is designed to provide nurses and other health care professionals with up-to-date informative texts on key professional and management issues and human skills in health care.

## Other books in the series

Spiritual Care: A resource guide

Budgeting Skills: A guide for nurse managers

Patients' Rights, Responsibilities and the Nurse

Measuring the Effectiveness of Nurse Education: The use of performance indicators

Employment Law for Nurses

Research Appreciation: An initial guide for nurses and health care professionals

Management Skills for Community Nurses

Portfolio Development and Profiling for Nurses, second edition

Central Health Studies

# Mental Health (Patients in the Community) Act 1995:

## *An introductory guide*

***Bridgit Dimond***
***Emeritus Professor of the University of Glamorgan***

Quay Books Division, Mark Allen Publishing Group,
Jesses Farm, Snow Hill,Dinton,
Nr Salisbury, Wiltshire, SP3 5HN



British Library Cataloguing-in-Publication Data
A catalogue record for this book is available from the British Library

ISBN 1 85642 012 4



Printed in the United Kingdom by Biddles Limited, Guildford

# Contents

# Abbreviations

| | |
|---|---|
| ASW | Approved social worker |
| CA | Court of appeal |
| CRMO | Community responsible medical officer |
| EL | Executive letter |
| HA | Health authority |
| HSG | Health service guidelines |
| LAC | Local authority circular |
| LSSA | Local social services authority |
| MHRT | Mental Health Review Tribunal |
| RMO | Responsible medical officer |
| RMP | Registered medical practitioner |

# List of Figures

# List of Tables

# Introduction

## Summary and aims of this booklet

This guide aims to provide a brief summary of the main points of the 1995 Act and to answer the concerns which have been raised about the Act. These are covered in part I of this booklet. Part II explains the amendments to sections 18 and 21 of the Mental Health Act 1983 and the legal situation of patients absent without leave. Part III discusses the amendments to section 17 of the Mental Health Act 1983 whereby a detained patient can be given leave of absence. A lists of references, further reading, useful addresses and an index are also provided. Many abbreviations are used and for convenience these are given at the beginning. The main sections of the 1995 Act are set out below in summary form so that the total coverage of the Act can be understood.

| Main sections of the 1995 Act | |
|---|---|
| **England and Wales:** | |
| Section 1 | After-care under supervision |
| Section 2 | Absence without leave |
| Section 3 | Leave of absence from hospital |
| **Scotland:** | |
| Section 4 | Community care orders |
| Section 5 | Absence without leave |
| Section 6 | Leave of absence from hospital |
| **Supplementary:** | |
| Section 7 | Short title, commencement and extent |
| Schedule 1 | After-care under supervision: supplementary |
| Schedule 2 | Community care orders: supplementary |

## Sources

The main sources for understanding the new provisions are: the Mental Health Act 1983, the Mental Health (Patients in the Community) Act 1995, the Statutory Instruments[1,2] and the guidance issued by the Department of Health and the Welsh Office[3]. Section 118 of the Mental Health Act (Code of Practice) is amended to require guidance to guardianship and after-care under supervision to be added to the other purposes. The guidance issued by the Department of Health and Welsh Office under this provision will eventually be incorporated into a revised Code of Practice.

# Part I

# After-care under supervision

## Background

The origins of the Mental Health (Patients in the Community) Act 1995 derive from the discussions relating to a community treatment order in the early 1990s. A report by the Royal College of Psychiatrists (RCP) in January 1993 proposed a community supervision order, amending earlier suggestions for a community treatment order. The House of Commons Select Committee which reported in June 1993 (Health Committee Session 1992–3, Fifth Report) did not support the RCP proposals and suggested instead further research into the use of guardianship and a major review of the 1983 Act.

In August 1993 an internal inquiry in the Department of Health set up by the Secretary of State reported that active consideration should be given to the introduction of supervised discharge over patients who presented a risk in the community. This recommendation was accepted by the Secretary of State and it became the first point of a Ten-Point Plan[4] published in August 1993 to allay the fears of the public in relation to the implementation of community care for severely mentally ill people — fears that had been fuelled by such incidents as the murder by Christopher Clunis[5] and the discovery of Ben Silcock, a mentally ill patient, in the lion's den at London Zoo. The ten points are shown in *Table 1*.

**Table 1: The Ten-Point Plan, August 1993**

| | |
|---|---|
| 1. | **STRONGER SUPERVISION** (This eventually led to the Mental Health (Patients in the Community) Act 1995) |
| 2. | **REVIEW OF 1983 ACT** (This is still awaited) |
| 3. | **REVISED CODE OF PRACTICE** (This came into force in November 1993) |
| 4. | **GUIDANCE ON DISCHARGE** (HSG(94)27 NHS Management Executive 1994) |
| 5. | **TRAINING FOR KEY WORKERS** (Left to individual authorities) |
| 6. | **BETTER INFO SYSTEMS OF PATIENTS AT RISK** (Supervision registers required to be kept from April 1994) |
| 7. | **REVIEW BY CLINICAL STANDARDS ADVISORY GROUP OF STANDARDS FOR SCHIZOPHRENIC PATIENTS** (Ongoing) |
| 8. | **MENTAL HEALTH TASK FORCE AND LOCALLY BASED CARE** (Ongoing) |
| 9. | **PURCHASING PLANS COVER MENTAL HEALTH SERVICES** (ie. the policy document Health of the Nations included a strategy for mental health services) |
| 10. | **IMPROVE MENTAL HEALTH SERVICES IN LONDON** (Ongoing) |

## 1. Aim of the Act

Section 117 of the Mental Health Act 1983 places a duty upon the health authority and local social services authority to provide, in conjunction with the voluntary sector, after-care services for certain patients who have been detained for treatment under the Mental Health Act 1983. The Mental Health (Patients in the Community) Act 1995 is designed to provide after-care under supervision for the patients who come within the provisions of section 117 to assist them in securing the after-care services to be provided under section 117. It also makes significant changes in the law relating to leave of absence and absence without leave. Separate provisions apply to Scotland (*Table 2*).

**Table 2: The Mental Health (Scotland) Act 1984**

Section 4 amends section 35 of the Mental Health (Scotland) Act 1984 to make provision for community care orders, as follows:

| | |
|---|---|
| S.35A | The community care order |
| S.35B | Procedure for the application |
| S.35C | The duration and renewal |
| S.35D | The variations of conditions in the order |
| S.35E | Change of special medical officer or after-care officer |
| S.35F | Appeal against community care order |
| S.35G | Admission to hospital for reassessment |
| S.35H | Reassessment: further provision |
| S.35I | Revocation of community care order |
| S.35J | Patients in custody or admitted to hospital in pursuance of emergency recommendations |

Section 5 amends sections 28, 30, 31, 32, 44, 47, 48, 49, 60 and 99 of the Mental Health (Scotland) Act 1984 in relation to absence without leave

Section 6 amends section 27 of the Mental Health (Scotland) Act 1984 in relation to leave of absence from hospital

The subsections relating to section 1 and the introduction of after-care under supervision are shown in *Table 3*. Section 1 makes amendments to section 25 of the 1983 Act so that the new provisions are incorporated into part 2 of the 1983 Act.

**Table 3: Summary of statutory provisions for after-care under supervision (S.1 of the 1995 Act)**

|  |  |
|---|---|
| 25A: | Applications for supervision: grounds and receipt |
| 25B: | Making of supervision application |
| 25C: | Supplementary provisions: mental disorder; right of examination; rectification of documents |
| 25D: | Requirements to secure receipt of after-care under supervision |
| 25E: | Review of after-care under supervision |
| 25F: | Reclassification of patients |
| 25G: | Duration and renewal of after-care under supervision |
| 25H: | Ending of after-care under supervision |
| 25I: | Special provisions for patients imprisoned or placed under section 2 |
| 25J | Patients moving from Scotland to England and Wales |

## 2. Grounds and criteria for application for after-care under supervision (S.25A)

Patients covered are shown in *Figure 1*.

A patient who has ceased to be liable to be detained for treatment (eg. on section 3) before the application for supervision is made cannot be placed under after-care under supervision. Thus if a patient was under section 3 and no after-care under supervision application was accepted while he or she was under section, and if, subsequently, that same patient was admitted under section 2 or as an informal patient, that patient cannot be placed under after-care under supervision.

**Figure 1: Persons eligible for after-care under supervision**

| | |
|---|---|
| **i.** | **Patients liable to be detained for treatment, ie patients under section 3, section 37, section 47 and section 48; and** |
| **ii.** | **who are 16 or over; and** |
| **iii.** | **who meet the criteria set out in section S.25A(4) (see *Figure 2*)** |

**Patients excluded:**

**patients under guardianship;**

**patients under a restriction order or direction;**

**informal patients or those under short-term sections (eg S.4, 5(2), 5(4), 135(1), 136) unless already under after-care under supervision).**

Patients who are under section 117 at present cannot be placed under after-care under supervision unless and until they are again admitted or transferred to hospital under section 3, 37, 47 or 48.

**Figure 2: Grounds for after-care under supervision (S.25A(4))**

**a.** **The patient is suffering from a specified form of mental disorder, ie mental illness, severe mental impairment, psychopathic disorder, or mental impairment (see *Figure 3*)**

**b.** **There would be a substantial risk of serious harm to:**

- **i. the health of the patient; or**
- **ii. the safety of the patient; or**
- **iii. the safety of other persons; or**
- **iv. of the patient being seriously exploited;**

**if he were not to receive the after-care services to be provided for him under section 117 after he leaves hospital; and**

**c.** **his being so subject to after-care under supervision is likely to help secure that he receives the after-care services to be so provided.**

From *Figure 2* it will be noted that there are three basic requirements before a patient, liable to be detained for treatment, can be placed under after-care under supervision.

## First requirement: a specific form of mental disorder

A specific form of mental illness is required before the patient can be admitted under section 3, 37, 47 or 48, and since liable to be detained for treatment is a prerequisite for after-care under supervision it follows logically that a specific form of mental disorder must also be present.

Both doctors supporting an application (ie. the applicant responsible medical officer and the doctor giving the medical recommendation, who cannot be the RMO) must agree on the same specific form of mental disorder, whether or not either cites another form as being present. *Figure 3* shows the definition of specific form of mental disorder.

**Figure 3: Specific forms of mental disorder S.1(2) Mental Health Act 1983**

**Mental illness — not further defined by statute;***

**Severe mental impairment: a state of arrested or incomplete development of mind which includes severe impairment of intelligence and social functioning and is associated with abnormally aggressive or seriously irresponsible conduct on the part of the person concerned;**

**Mental impairment: a state of arrested or incomplete development of mind (not amounting to severe mental impairment) which includes significant impairment of intelligence and social functioning and is associated with abnormally aggressive or seriously irresponsible conduct on the part of the person concerned;**

**Psychopathic disorder: a persistent disorder or disability of mind (whether or not including significant impairment of intelligence) which results in abnormally aggressive or seriously irresponsible conduct on the part of the person concerned.**

* Mental illness has no statutory definition although in one case[8] the Court of Appeal defined the appropriate tests as 'What would the ordinary sensible person have said about the patient's condition in this case if he had been informed of his behaviour...?' Hoggett has described this as 'the man-must-be-mad' approach.[9]

### Second requirement: substantial risk of a, b, or c if after-care services were not received

#### *Substantial risk*

This is not statutorily defined, but there would have to be a strong possibility of risk based on the previous history and knowledge of the patient.

#### *Serious harm*

Trivial incidents could presumably be ignored; however, the difficulty is that while serious harm may not be the intention, even a minor injury could prove, because of the circumstances, to be extremely serious.

It should be noted that serious harm can relate to four distinct possibilities: three relating to the patient, and the other to the safety of other persons.

Health of the patient could include the danger of neglect and lack of personal care, as well as anxieties more specifically concerned with the patient's mental and physical health, eg the need to take regular medication for a physical illness or medication for mental disorder.

#### *Serious exploitation*

This term is not defined and it widens the scope of the after-care under supervision to include protection for persons such as those suffering from elderly mental infirmity as well as those with learning disabilities. Those suffering from mental impairment or serious mental impairment can only be detained for treatment if the impairment is associated with abnormally aggressive or seriously irresponsible conduct.

#### *Serious harm to the safety of other persons*

A risk assessment would list the criteria that would have to be used to decide whether there was a substantial risk of this arising. The discharge guidance of the NHS Management

Executive[6] sets out the criteria that could be used. It suggests that a full assessment of risk should include:

- past history of the patient;
- self-reporting by the patient at interview;
- observation of the behaviour and mental state of the patient;
- discrepancies between what is reported and what is observed;
- psychological and, if appropriate, physiological tests;
- statistics derived from studies of related cases;
- prediction indicators derived from research[7].

**Third requirement: After-care under supervision is likely to help to secure that he receives the after-care services to be so provided**

This third requirement might become one of the main determinants for not using after-care under supervision.

It may be, for example, that the patient makes it absolutely clear that he will not comply with any after-care plan or with any requirements. It may be that the previous history of the patient gives evidence of this non-compliance. In such circumstances, the statutory grounds would appear not to be present, and therefore the patient could not be placed under supervision. Furthermore, it would appear that there should be a reasonable belief that this ground is satisfied before the patient is discharged under after-care under supervision, since in the absence of any reasonable belief that the patient would comply with the requirements and/or the after-care services, a person with substantial risk of serious harm will be unsupervised in the community.

It would therefore seem that the alternative to discharge under supervision for such a patient would either be continued detention or guardianship (see below). The patient's consent to after-care under supervision is not required, although the patient must be consulted and his or her views taken into account. However, a clear objection by the patient to the possibility of after-care under supervision may well defeat its object of helping him or her to secure his or her receiving section 117 after-care services.

Could after-care under supervision be tried on an experimental basis where there is no realistic belief that it will succeed in ensuring that the patient receives the section 117 after-care services? The answer would appear to be no, unless there is a reasonable belief that this third requirement is met.

The definitions of the specific forms of mental disorder are shown in *Figure 3*.

## 3. Procedure for application (S.25B)

The RMO is the applicant. He or she completes form 1S setting out that the criteria and grounds are met. There are no provisions for the duty to be delegated or for a nominee to be appointed as under section 5(3). If the RMO were on holiday, could his senior registrar make an application, or would the applicant have to be another consultant? The RMO is defined in the 1983 Act as the registered medical practitioner in charge of the treatment of the patient (S.34(1)(a)). This would normally be a doctor of consultant status.

Since the process of application could take some time, it is unlikely to be an emergency procedure and the RMO could plan well ahead. In exceptional circumstances, if the usual RMO of the patient was away but another person had been temporarily appointed as the RMO, then this latter person would be able to be the applicant.

Consultations must be carried out before the application is signed. The persons to be consulted are shown in *Figure 4*.

**Figure 4: Persons to be consulted about the application (S.25B)**

1. **Patient;**
2. **1 or more persons who have been professionally concerned with the patient's medical treatment in hospital;**
3. **1 or more persons who will be professionally concerned with the after-care services to be provided for the patient under S.117;**
4. **Any person who, the RMO believes, will play a substantial part in the care of the patient after he leaves hospital but will not be professionally concerned with any of the after-care services to be so provided;**
5. **The person appearing to be the nearest relative (subject to the qualified right of the patient to prevent) (see *Figures 30* and *31*).**

**Who does the consultation?**

The Act is very carefully worded: the consultation must take place and the RMO must take into account the views which are expressed, but there is no specific requirement that the RMO actually carries out the consultation him or herself. (A similar wording is used for the consultation which must precede a renewal of after-care under supervision, where the CRMO must take into account the views expressed in the consultation.)

It would be good practice that where someone other than the RMO carries out the consultation, a record should be made of the views expressed so that they can be taken into account by the RMO before he or she makes the application. This may cause some difficulties if, for example, the person who is defined as the substantial part player does not wish to have his or her views written down. In addition it should be noted that it is for the RMO to decide who this person is likely to be: it is the belief of the RMO which is required by the Act.

## Procedure on receipt of application

The application is submitted to the health authority or delegated body, usually the NHS trust.

### *What does receipt mean?*

The managers of the NHS trust or other body to whom the HA has delegated the responsibility would appoint an officer who will be responsible for receiving the application, checking that it is in order and that all the accompanying reports, etc are present.

## Consultation with the Local Social Services Authority

Before the application is accepted, the HA (or body to whom these functions are delegated) must consult with the LSSA. The application is accompanied by the written recommendation of the approved social worker, but it is still a statutory requirement for the LSSA to be consulted.

### *What does this mean?*

Even though the LSSA would have been consulted in the formulation of the after-care plan, represented at the section 117 meeting and consulted about the advisability of after-care under supervision, a further formal consultation is still required. It could therefore be that the LSSA strongly counsels against after-care under supervision. Yet the Act does not require the LSSA to agree to the application. Clearly, however, the views of the LSSA which were hostile to the application should be taken into account.

It may be, for example, that the LSSA stated that the after-care services could not be resourced. Ideally, however, those social workers involved in the after-care planning and attending the section 117 meetings should have advised on whether the plans could be resourced. It would appear too that if the multidisciplinary team had agreed on an after-care plan and supported the application for after-care under supervision, the refusal of the LSSA to resource it when consulted formally on receipt of the application would be *prima-facie* evidence of a breach of section 117 by the LSSA, and could be the basis of court action by the patient using the precedent of the case brought by Mr Fox against Ealing Health Authority and Social Services Authority[10].

**Procedure after the application is accepted.**

Once accepted, the HA or provider unit must inform the persons shown in *Figure 5*.

| Figure 5: Informing after application is accepted (S.25A(8)): | |
|---|---|
| 1. | The patient (orally and in writing); |
| 2. | Any person consulted prior to the application whose name is included in the application form; |
| 3. | The person consulted as the nearest relative (if not barred by the patient). |

The patient must be told orally and in writing that the application has been accepted and also the effect of the after-care under supervision and in particular his or her rights to apply to a Mental Health Review Tribunal. Leaflets will be available to give to the patient on the acceptance of the application and the person designated with the responsibility of telling the patient the information should have the necessary training and knowledge to be able to answer the patient's questions. It would be useful if a form could be designed to record the giving of this information similar to that which many NHS trusts now have for the giving of information under section 132.

## Following the acceptance of the after-care under supervision application

What if the patient remains under section 3 or 37 when the application is accepted? There are several different scenarios which could follow the acceptance of the application:

1. The patient is in hospital under section 3 etc and stays on in hospital under section 3 for the time being.
2. The patient is in hospital under section 3 etc and is immediately discharged from the section and becomes informal and remains in hospital.
3. The patient is in hospital under section 3 etc and the section ends and the patient is discharged.
4. The patient is on section 17 leave and continues under section 3 for some time after the application is accepted.
5. The patient is on section 17 leave and section 3 is ended by the RMO immediately the application is accepted.

In all of these situations the six months of the after-care under supervision commences at the time of the acceptance of the application by the HA (or trust), but the actual provisions of after-care do not come into force until the patient leaves hospital and ceases to be liable to be detained for treatment. It follows therefore that a patient who is on section 17 leave will continue to be liable to be detained and the after-care under supervision arrangements do not commence until the section under which he or she is liable to be detained is ended. The six months' duration of the after-care under supervision, however, commences when the application is accepted. In some cases, therefore, there may be only a few months or weeks of the after-care under supervision left to run when the section under which the patient is detained ends.

Notification to the RMO that the application has been accepted is essential. If the RMO submits the application for after-care under supervision, and, falsely believing it to have been accepted, takes the patient off section 3 (or its equivalent) before the application is accepted, the patient is no longer liable to be detained. In this situation, if the application were to be in any way defective, it would be too late for it to be resubmitted, since the patient is no longer liable to be detained.

## 4. Check list

A check list for the applications is shown in *Figure 6*.

**Figure 6: Check list for after-care under supervision application**

**1. Application form stating that:**

- **i. patient is liable to be detained for treatment;**
- **ii. patient is 16 or over;**
- **iii. conditions of S.25A(4) are satisfied (*see Figure 2*) ie**
  - **a. specified form of mental disorder;**
  - **b. substantial risk of serious harm... if after-care services not given;**
  - **c. being under supervision is likely to secure that he gets the after-care services;**
- **iv. consultations have been carried out and have been taken into account (see *Figure 4*);**
- **v. written recommendation of a doctor (other than the RMO);**
- **vi. written recommendation of ASW;**
- **vii. signed statement by CRMO;**
- **viii. signed statement by supervisor;**
- **ix. list of after-care services to be provided;**
- **x. requirements stipulated under S.25D (see *Figure 7*).**

The medical records officer is likely to have the responsibility of ensuring that all the paperwork is properly completed and the correct documents submitted. The right to rectify the documents given by section 25C(6) permits the rectification to take place within 14 days, but only with the consent of the HA (or delegated body) to whom the application is submitted (see *Figure 38*).

### 5. Requirements (S.25D)

These are shown in *Figure 7*.

**Figure 7: Requirements under section 25D(3)**

- **i.** **that the patient reside at a specified place;**
- **ii.** **that the patient attend at specified places and times for the purpose of medical treatment, occupation, education or training; and**
- **iii.** **that access to the patient be given, at any place where the patient is residing, to the supervisor, any registered medical practitioner, or any ASW or to any person authorised by supervisor.**

**How specific should the requirements set out in *Figure 7* be?**

They must be sufficiently clear to enable the patient to understand what is required of him or her and to enable them to be enforced, if necessary (see below). However, if they are too specific, considerable difficulties could occur if amendments were necessary. These requirements can be changed following consultation and review by the HA under section 25E (see below). However, if the times, for example, of the day centre visits were changed it would seem inappropriate to go through the consultation procedure set out under section 25D(6). It is suggested that the requirement could be 'attend at the day centre once a week, the day to be agreed between the patient, supervisor and centre'.

### Enforcement of requirements

Section 25D(4) gives powers to enforce the requirement of residence and attendance as set out in *Figure 8*.

**Figure 8: Powers to enforce requirements**

**A patient subject to after-care under supervision may be taken and conveyed by, or by any person authorised by, the supervisor to any place where the patient is required to reside or to attend for the purpose of medical treatment, occupation, education or training.**

Refusal to permit access to a supervisor or other authorised person is an offence under section 129 of the Mental Health Act 1983 as amended by the 1995 Act.

### Example of enforcement

The patient goes missing from the place of residence specified in the requirements under section 25D(3). If necessary the police could be asked to search for the patient and return the patient to the specified place of residence. In this way it is possible to keep firm control on the whereabouts of patients under after-care under supervision which is not possible in the case of section 117 patients who are not under after-care under supervision.

### Conveying the patient to the place of attendance

The decision as to whether there should be compulsion to take the patient to the specified place is a question for the professional judgment of the supervisor in conjunction with the CRMO and other professional colleagues. It may be, for example, in the case of a patient suffering from learning disabilities or an elderly, mentally infirm patient that while he or she would not go on his or her own, he or she would attend if prompted and conveyed there and would in fact benefit from the attendance and stay there. In such cases, compulsion may be justified.

## Right of access

It is an offence for a person to refuse access by an appropriate person to a patient who is under after-care under supervision. The person requiring access shall, if asked to do so, produce some duty authenticated document to show that he or she is a person entitled to be given access to the patient. However, this person has no right to force entry into the premises.

### *What if access is refused?*

The person refusing access is guilty of an offence under section 129 (as amended). The person requiring access would notify the supervisor and/or the CRMO. It is possible that a warrant could be obtained under section 135(1) if the conditions for that section were satisfied. It would not appear that a warrant could be obtained under section 135(2) since a patient under after-care under supervision is not liable to be detained. The power to convey the patient to the specified place of residence does not imply the right to force entry onto another person's premises.

The most important effect of the patient's failure to comply with the requirements or accept the after-care services is that this automatically triggers off the need to undertake a review of after-care under supervision.

In applying section 135(1) to a patient under after-care under supervision to whom access is being refused, it is a question of the individual circumstances as to whether he or she is being neglected or is being kept otherwise than under proper control. It may be that failure to comply with any requirements stipulated in the after-care under supervision plan is evidence of lack of proper control and failure to take medication could be seen as neglect.

***Will the right to enforce the requirements damage the therapeutic relationship developed between the supervisor and the patient?***

It has been stated[11] that it is feared that having the power to enforce attendance etc will seriously undermine the therapeutic relationship between professional and patient. However, similar fears were expressed to the author while undertaking research into the use and effect of section 5(4) of the Act. Much depends upon the personalities of those concerned. Since there is always the possibility of the supervisor initiating an examination with a view to the patient being readmitted under section, and this applies to all patients under section 117 as well as those under guardianship and those who have been admitted informally in the past, it is doubtful if the powers to enforce the requirements set under after-care under supervision will have a negative effect on the relationship. In practice there may be little attempt to enforce the requirements, since there seems little point in compelling the patient to attend a day centre or similar venue if, when there, he or she refuses to participate in the activities or stay. There is no power to keep the patient there unwillingly, although the patient can in theory be returned there each time he or she leaves.

## 6. Review (S.25E)

### a. Regular review

Under section 25E(1) the after-care services and the requirements imposed on a patient who is subject to after-care under supervision shall be kept under review, and (where appropriate) modified, by the responsible after-care bodies. *This duty cannot be delegated by the HA and the LSSA.*

### b. Review triggered by actions of the patient

In the case of a patient who neglects or refuses to receive any or all of the after-care services provided under section 117 or to comply with any or all of the requirements imposed under section 25D, the responsible after-care bodies *shall* review, and where appropriate modify, either the after-care services provided or any requirements.

The HA and the LSSA are the responsible after-care bodies and this duty under sections 25E(1) and (3) cannot be delegated.

#### *How soon should the review be initiated?*

Taken literally, the review commences the first time a patient neglects to receive or refuses to comply. In practice the supervisor and/or CRMO will use professional discretion in interpreting the circumstances as to whether a review is appropriate. For example, a patient may refuse to attend industrial therapy on the grounds that he has a headache. The supervisor might not believe this to be true, but may give him the benefit of the doubt, and would monitor the situation carefully to be sure that the patient is not neglecting or refusing because his mental state has deteriorated.

#### *How is a review set up?*

It has been emphasised that the HA and LSSA cannot delegate the duties under sections 25D(1) and (3) to review and modify after-care under supervision. Each HA must set up its own procedure, in agreement with its providers:

a. for it to review and modify (where appropriate) the after-care services and requirements for patients under after-care under supervision (ie time limits would have to be set for regular review); and

b. for it to be informed if and when the patient has neglected to receive or refused to comply with the requirements.

The HA must then consider whether the after-care services or the requirements should be modified.

### *What are the effects of a review?*

The following could result:

a. No change to either the after-care services or the requirements;

b. Modifications to either or both;

c. The HA and LSSA inform the CRMO if they conclude that it is appropriate for the patient to cease to be subject to after-care under supervision; and

d. The HA and LSSA inform an ASW, if they conclude that it might be appropriate for the patient to be readmitted to a hospital for treatment.

*Figure 9* summarises the reasons for a review.

**Figure 9: Review triggered by patient's actions**

**The review MUST be initiated when a patient under after-care under supervision refuses or neglects:**

**a. to receive any or all of the after-care services provided for him under S.117; or**

**b. to comply with any or all of any requirements imposed on him under S.25D.**

### Consultations prior to modification of after-care services or requirements

The consultations needed before modification of after-care services or requirements are shown in *Figure 10*.

| **Figure 10: Consultations following review and before modifications are made:** | |
|---|---|
| **a.** | **the patient;** |
| **b.** | **any person who the responsible after-care bodies believe plays (or will play) a substantial part in the care of the patient but is not professionally concerned with the after-care services provided for the patient under S.117;** |
| **c.** | **the person (if any) appearing to be the nearest relative (with the qualified right of the patient to request that there is no consultation with the nearest relative).** |

### *Who does the consultation?*

While the regulations state that the responsible after-care bodies cannot delegate the duty to review, and if appropriate modify, it does not follow that the task of consulting cannot be delegated; it may therefore be appropriate for the NHS trust health professionals or the social services professionals to undertake the consultation. If this occurs, then there must be written evidence of the views expressed so that these can be taken into account in deciding whether the modifications should be made.

### *Procedure following modification of after-care services or requirements*

Following the review, if modifications are made then the action shown in *Figure 11* must be taken by the responsible after-care bodies (although these tasks can be delegated).

| **Figure 11: Action following modification** | |
|---|---|
| **Where the health authority or social services authority modifies the after-care services or requirements they shall:** | |
| **a.** | **inform the patient both orally and in writing;** |
| **b.** | **inform anyone consulted as the substantial part player about the modifications;** |
| **c.** | **inform the person consulted as the nearest relative.** |

## 7. Duration and renewal (S.25G)

As in section 3, the time of after-care under supervision lasts initially for six months from the date of the acceptance of the application, and can be renewed for a further six months and then for one year at a time.

The procedure for renewal is shown in *Figure 12*.

| Figure 12: Procedure for renewal | |
|---|---|
| **1.** | **Examination of patient by CRMO;** |
| **2.** | **CRMO satisfied that conditions set out in S.25G4 are complied with (see *Figure 13*)** |
| **3.** | **CRMO takes into account views expressed in consultations (*see Figure 14*);** |
| **4.** | **Report to HA/provider in the prescribed form.** |

### How and when can a renewal take place?

Not more than two months before the supervision is due to come to an end, it is the duty of the CRMO:

a. to examine the patient; and

b. if it appears to him that the conditions set out in subsection (4) of section 25G (*Figure 13*) are complied with, to furnish to the responsible after-care bodies a report to that effect in the prescribed form.

**Figure 13: Conditions for renewal of after-care under supervision (S.25G(4))**

**a.** the patient is suffering from a specified form of mental disorder;

**b.** there would be a substantial risk of serious harm:

to the health or

to the safety of the patient or

to the safety of other persons, or

of the patient being seriously exploited,

if he were not to receive the after-care services provided for him under section 117;

**c.** his being subject to after-care under supervision is likely to help to secure that he receives the after-care services so provided.

The CRMO shall not consider that the conditions shown in *Figure 13* are complied with unless the consultations shown in *Figure 14* have been carried out.

**Figure 14: Consultations prior to renewal (S.25G(5))**

**a.**
- i. the patient;
- ii. the supervisor;
- iii. 1 or more persons professionally concerned with the patient's medical treatment (unless there is no-one other than the CRMO);
- iv. 1 or more persons professionally concerned with the after-care services (other than medical treatment) provided for the patient under S.117; and
- v. any person whom the CRMO believes plays a substantial part in the care of the patient but is not professionally concerned with the after-care services so provided;

**b.** such steps as are practicable are taken to consult the person (if any) appearing to be the nearest relative (subject to the qualified right of the patient to block);

**c.** the CRMO has taken into account any relevant views expressed by the persons consulted.

### Action to be taken following renewal

The responsible after-care bodies must take the action shown in *Figure 15.*

**Figure 15: Action following renewal**

**The responsible after-care bodies shall:**

**a. inform the patient both orally and in writing:**
- **i. that the report has been furnished; and**
- **ii. of the effect in his case and his rights (including the right of appealing to an MHRT);**

**b. inform any person consulted as the substantial part player; and**

**c. inform any person consulted as the nearest relative that the report has been furnished.**

## 8. Ending after-care under supervision (S.25H)

*Figure 16* sets out the main ways in which after-care under supervision can come to an end.

**Figure 16: Ending of after-care under supervision:**

**a. by CRMO;**
**b. by admission for treatment under S.3;**
**c. by being received into guardianship under S.7;**
**d. by the MHRT;**
**e. by lapse of time and no renewal.**

### Ending after-care supervision by the CRMO

The CRMO may at any time direct that a patient subject to after-care under supervision shall cease to be so subject. However, he cannot do so unless the requirements in relation to consultation have been carried out under section 25H(3) (*Figure 17*).

### *Who must be consulted?*

The list of those who must be consulted is shown in *Figure 17.*

**Figure 17: Consultations for ending after-care under supervision**

**a.**
- **i. the patient;**
- **ii. the supervisor;**
- **iii. 1 or more persons professionally concerned with the patient's medical treatment (unless there is no-one other than the CRMO);**
- **iv. 1 or more persons who are professionally concerned with the after-care services (other than medical treatment) provided for the patient under S.117;**
- **v. any person who the CRMO believes plays a substantial part in the care of the patient but is not professionally concerned with the after-care services so provided;**

**b. such steps as are practicable have been taken to consult the person (if any) appearing to be the nearest relative of the patient about the giving of the direction to end supervision (subject to the qualified right of the patient to block) (see *Figures 30* and *31*);**

**c. the CRMO has taken into account any views expressed by the persons consulted.**

### What action must be taken after the ending (for any reason) of supervision?

Where after-care under supervision ends, the responsible after-care bodies must take the action shown in *Figure 18.*

**Figure 18: Action to be taken by responsible after-care bodies when supervision ends**

| | |
|---|---|
| **a.** | **inform the patient both orally and in writing;** |
| **b.** | **inform any person who they believe plays a substantial part in the care of the patient but is not professionally concerned with the after-care services provided under S.117; and** |
| **c.** | **take such steps as are practicable to inform, in writing, the person (if any) appearing to be the nearest relative of the patient (this does not apply if the patient's objection to the nearest relative being told was not overruled) that the patient has ceased to be subject to after-care under supervision.** |

## 9. Reclassification (S.25F)

While the basic principles for the reclassification of the form of mental disorder are similar to the provisions of section 16, where the specific form of mental disorder is reclassified for a patient who is subject to after-care under supervision, consultation must take place by the CRMO with one or more persons who are concerned with the patient's medical treatment, if they exist. Following the report on reclassification being furnished to the HA (or its delegatee), the responsible after-care bodies must inform the persons shown in *Figure 19*.

**Figure 19: Action following reclassification (S.25F(4))**

**The responsible after-care bodies shall inform:**

| | |
|---|---|
| **a.** | **the patient (orally and in writing);** |
| **b.** | **the person appearing to be the nearest relative of the patient (subject to the qualified right of the patient to object);** |

**that the report has been furnished.**

If it appears to the CRMO that a patient is suffering from a form of mental disorder different from the one specified in the application for after-care under supervision, he may furnish a report to that effect to the HA (or its delegated body). The effect of the report is that the application is treated as though the new form of mental disorder were specified in it. The HA (or delegated body) must then take the action shown in *Figure 19*.

The importance of the action shown in *Figure 19* is that reclassification triggers the right of the patient to apply to an MHRT.

## 10. Application to a Mental Health Review Tribunal (Schedule 1 paragraphs 7–12)

The opportunities for the patient and/or nearest relative to apply to an MHRT are shown in *Figure 20*.

**Figure 20: Applications to an MHRT**

**The right to apply to an MHRT exists:**

**a.** **when the supervision application is accepted;**

**b.** **when the specific form of mental disorder from which the patient is suffering is reclassified;**

**c.** **when the supervision application is renewed.**

**NB. The Secretary of State may refer to MHRT at any time after the patient is placed under after-care under supervision.**

The RMP can require production and inspection of any records of after-care services provided.

### Powers of MHRT

The MHRT has the powers shown in *Figure 21*.

**Figure 21: Powers of the MHRT**

**A. The MHRT MUST direct that the patient shall cease to be subject to after-care under supervision:**

- **a. if the conditions set by S.25A4 (see *Figure 2*) are not complied with when the patient is still in hospital; and**
- **b. if the conditions set by S.25G4 (see *Figure 13*) are not complied with when the patient has left hospital.**

**B. The MHRT can:**

1. **direct that the patient shall cease to be subject to after-care under supervision;**
2. **recommend that the RMO consider whether to make a supervision application, in cases where the tribunal does not direct the discharge of the patient (under S.48);**
3. **amend application etc where satisfied that patient's mental disorder should be reclassified.**

The time limits for bringing an application to the MHRT are shown in *Figure 22*.

**Figure 22: Time limits for bringing an MHRT application**

**Time limits for bringing an MHRT case:**

- **a. application — six months from acceptance.**
- **b. reclassification — 28 days from the report being furnished.**
- **c. renewal — the time that the renewal of the after-care under supervision lasts.**

## Is legal aid available?

A patient is able to obtain legal aid on a non-means tested basis for applications before the MHRT.

## 11. Community responsible medical officer

At all times while the patient is subject to after-care under supervision, his or her medical treatment must be in the care of a section 12 doctor who is known as the CRMO. This person may also be the RMO. Guidance suggests that the CRMO should be a consultant psychiatrist but a doctor who is section 12 approved may also be appropriate as the CRMO.

- The CRMO may be the RMO
- The CRMO may be a consultant psychiatrist employed by an NHS trust
- The CRMO may be a section 12 approved GP. (The guidance (paragraph 44) recommends that the right person to undertake the role would be a consultant psychiatrist.)

The only statutory requirements are that the CRMO is:

1. A registered medical practitioner
2. Section 12 approved
3. In charge of the medical treatment provided for the patient as part of the section 117 after-care services.

The duties of the CRMO are shown in *Figure 23*.

**Figure 23: Duties of the CRMO:**

1. **The CRMO is in charge of the medical treatment provided for the patient as part of the S.117 services; he must provide a signed statement to that effect before the application for after-care under supervision can be accepted;**
2. **Should provide a written recommendation for after-care supervision (if different from the RMO);**
3. **The CRMO has the responsibility of considering whether the after-care under supervision should be renewed and ensuring that all the consultation provisions take place and are taken into account;**
4. **The CRMO has responsibility for arranging for the reclassification of the specific form of mental disorder from which the patient is suffering, if appropriate;**
5. **The CRMO, together with the supervisor, would have the responsibility of bringing the need for a review to the attention of the health authority and social services authority;**
6. **The CRMO can at any time end the after-care under supervision, but must ensure that the necessary consultations take place before doing so.**

### At all times — the doctor

The HA has a duty (which can be delegated to the provider) to secure that at all times the medical care of the patient under after-care under supervision is undertaken by a section 12 doctor. There are no statutory provisions for the delegation of the work of the CRMO, but there are provisions for changing the name of the CRMO (see below). In practice the CRMO will set up a deputising system for cover at weekends and holidays, but the doctor who deputises must be section 12 approved.

## Changing the name of the CRMO

If another person becomes the CRMO for the patient the action shown in *Figure 24* must be taken by the responsible after-care bodies (or their delegatees).

**Figure 24: Changing the name of the CRMO**

**The health authority and social services bodies (or those to whom they delegate the duty) must:**

**a. inform the patient both orally and in writing;**

**b. inform any person they believe to play a substantial part in the care of the patient who is not professionally concerned with the after-care services provided under S.117;**

**c. take such steps as are practicable to inform in writing the nearest relative (unless the patient otherwise requests).**

## 12. The supervisor

Paragraph 15 of schedule 1 requires the HA to secure that at all times while a patient is subject to after-care under supervision:

- a person professionally concerned with any of the after-care services to be so provided is supervising him or her with a view to securing that he or she receives the after-care services so provided.

There is no further statutory definition, although the guidance (paragraph 43) suggests that 'the supervisor must be a suitably qualified and experienced member of the patient's care team in the community.' The guidance (paragraph 43) also suggests that the person 'has agreed to take on this role'. This is considered below.

***Professionally concerned:*** This means being paid to undertake duties in connection with the patient's care. It does not necessarily require that the person is a registered professional. Thus an occupational therapy assistant could be designated as the supervisor, although he or she would have to have the necessary training and experience to undertake the work of supervision. No particular professions are cited, although it is likely that the (approved) social worker or community psychiatric nurse members of the team will most frequently be appointed as supervisors.

### Functions of the supervisor

The statutory responsibility of the supervisor is to supervise 'with a view to securing that the patient receives the after-care services' provided under section 117.

The duties of the supervisor are shown in *Figure 25*.

**Figure 25: Duties of the supervisor**

**The following duties are implied by the statutory definition:**

- **a.** **to visit the patient (powers of access are given under S.25D and discussed above);**
- **b.** **to check that the patient is receiving the after-care services;**
- **c.** **to check that the patient is complying with the requirements set out under S.25D;**
- **d.** **to request a review if the patient neglects to obtain the after-care services or refuses to comply with the requirements.**

**In addition the guidance (paragraph 43) suggests that the supervisor will:**

- **a.** **ensure that the team reviews the after-care plan well before the date when it falls to be reviewed, and whenever any shortfall in the arrangements is identified;**
- **b.** **have close working links with the CRMO;**
- **c.** **be supported by a proper framework of training, accountability and clear reporting lines within his or her employing authority.**

### Powers of the supervisor

a. The supervisor can require access to the patient or authorise any other person to have access (see above)

b. The supervisor has powers, and can authorise any other person, to convey the patient to the specified place of residence or to any other place to which the patient is required to go under the requirements set under section 25D.

### Changing the supervisor

If another person becomes the supervisor for the patient the action shown in *Figure 26* must be taken by the responsible after-care bodies (or their delegatees).

**Figure 26: Changing the name of the supervisor**

**The health authority and social services bodies (or those to whom they delegate the duty) must:**

**a. inform the patient both orally and in writing;**

**b. inform any person they believe to play a substantial part in the care of the patient who is not professionally concerned with the after-care services provided under section 117;**

**c. take such steps as are practicable to inform in writing the nearest relative (unless the patient otherwise requests).**

### Training for being a supervisor

The Ten-Point plan (see page 2) recommended that key workers should receive training for their role, but it has been left to individual social service departments and NHS providers to arrange such training. Many supervisors will have experience as a key worker and some additional training for the role of a supervisor will be necessary, particularly on the legal requirements of after-care under supervision. Where the person to be appointed as supervisor has never been a key worker, clearly extra training will be necessary.

### At all times — supervisor

A patient under after-care under supervision must have a supervisor at all times. A standard procedure exists for the change of name of the supervisor (see below). However, this would be inappropriate if the supervisor is simply going on holiday or away for a weekend. There are no statutory powers to designate a deputy comparable to those under section 5(3) where the RMO can nominate a deputy for the purposes of section 5(2) (detaining an informal patient for up to 72 hours). Local arrangements must, however, exist for there to be a supervisor at all times for the patient. This may mean the setting up of an on-call system for the community nursing service. It may mean the use of the out-of-hours service run by the social services emergency mental health care team. It will certainly mean close working between social services and the health service provider, whether the supervisor is appointed from social services or from health services.

The patient and the substantial part-player in the care of the patient and others caring for the patient should also know who is the supervisor or covering for the supervisor at all times. This means ensuring that the on-call system is easily accessed by those who may have concerns about the patient or by the patient himself or herself.

#### *Can a professional concerned with the after-care of the patient refuse to be the supervisor?*

The guidance suggests that the supervisor must have agreed to supervise. However, it is submitted here that no professional with the appropriate training and experience could refuse on principle ever to be a supervisor. An employee has an implied duty under the contract of employment to obey the reasonable instructions of the employer. If, therefore, an employee was asked to be a supervisor it is suggested that it would be unreasonable for an employee, who was of the right grade and had the appropriate experience, to refuse on the grounds that he or she disagreed with the concept of supervision and would never be a supervisor. Such a refusal would be a breach of the implied term and disciplinary action could be taken against such an employee.

On the other hand it might be entirely reasonable for an employee to state that because he or she disagreed with a particular patient being discharged, he or she was not prepared to supervise, that there was a personality difficulty between that potential supervisor and that particular patient, that the particular employee had not had sufficient training to be a supervisor, or that the existing workload of the member of staff in question did not permit him or her to undertake the work involved in after-care under supervision, unless additional resources were provided. The case of Mr Fox[10] shows that the court would not order a particular doctor to supervise a patient against the doctor's will where the doctor's refusal arises from an honestly held clinical judgment that the treatment is not in the patient's best interests or is not in the best interests of the community in which the supervision would take place.

## 13. Patients' rights:

*Figure 27* summarises the occasions on which the patient must be consulted and *Figure 28* summarises the occasions on which the patient must be informed. Information must be given to the patient orally and in writing. A written leaflet is available but there must also be clear delegation to a person to provide information orally. *Figure 29* summarises the rights of the patient in relation to after-care under supervision.

**Figure 27: Consulting the patient**

| | |
|---|---|
| 1. | Before the application for after-care under supervision is submitted (S.25B(2)(a)(i)); |
| 2. | Before modifications are made to the after-care services and/or requirements (S.25E(6)(a)); |
| 3. | When the CRMO is considering whether or not to renew the after-care under supervision (S.25G(5)(a)); |
| 4. | When the CRMO is considering ending after-care under supervision (S.25H(3)(a)(i)). |

**Figure 28 : Informing the patient**

| | |
|---|---|
| 1. | After the application for after-care under supervision is accepted (S.25A(8)(a)); |
| 2. | After modifications have been made to the after-care services and/or requirements (S.25E(8)(a)); |
| 3. | When the form of mental disorder from which the patient is suffering has been reclassified (S.25F(4)(a)); |
| 4. | When the CRMO and/or supervisor is changed (S.25E(11)(a)); |
| 5. | When after-care under supervision is renewed (S.25G(8)(a)); |
| 6. | When after-care under supervision is ended (for whatever reason) (S.25H(6)(a)). |

**Figure 29: Patients' rights in relation to after-care under supervision**

- **To be consulted (see *Figure 27*)**
- **To be informed (see *Figure 28*)**
- **To object to the nearest relative being consulted or informed (see *Figure 30*), subject to the right of the RMO or CRMO to overrule this objection**
- **To have a CRMO at all times when subject to after-care under supervision**
- **To have a supervisor at all times when subject to after-care under supervision**
- **To have after-care services provided under S.117**

In certain cases, the patient has a qualified right to prevent the nearest relative being informed or consulted. These occasions are shown in *Figure 30*.

**Figure 30: Patient's qualified right to prevent the contact with the nearest relative**

1. **Consultation on application (S.25B(3));**
2. **Where the after-care under supervision is being reviewed and consideration is taking place on the modifications to the after-care services and/or requirements (S.25E(7));**
3. **Where the CRMO and/or supervisor is changed (S.25E(11)(c));**
4. **Where the specific form of mental disorder is reclassified (S.25F(4)(b));**
5. **Where renewal is being considered (S.25G(6));**
6. **Where considerations on the ending of after-care under supervision are taking place (S.25H(4)).**

**How should the patient be informed?**

The Act requires that the patient is given information both by word of mouth and in writing. Leaflets are available for handing out to the patient explaining after-care under supervision. The person who is given the task of speaking to the patient must have due regard to the patient's level of understanding and must take account of any physical or mental limitations, eg. language and handicap, eg. blindness or deafness. The person must have had the training to understand the principles of after-care under supervision and be able to answer the patient's questions. It must be clear who has this delegated task to ensure that the information is given as required. It may be advisable to record the date and time and the results of the information being given. It may be necessary to repeat the process if it is felt that the patient may understand more at a subsequent interview.

The leaflets provided by the Department of Health will presumably eventually be translated into different languages as required.

The importance of giving the patient the information cannot be exaggerated since the patient needs the information to exercise his or her right to apply to the MHRT.

The right shown in *Figure 30* can be overruled if the factors shown in *Figure 31* exist.

## 14. Role of the nearest relative

The nearest relative must be consulted or informed on the occasions shown in *Figure 28* and *29* unless the patient objects and that objection is not overruled on the grounds shown in *Figure 31*.

| **Figure 31: Overruling the objection by the patient to contact with the nearest relative** | |
|---|---|
| **a.** | **the patient has a propensity to violent or dangerous behaviour towards others; and** |
| **b.** | **the RMO or CRMO (where relevant) considers that it is appropriate for steps to be taken to contact the nearest relative.** |

**What if the nearest relative is also the person who is believed to be likely to play a substantial part in the after-care of the patient?**

The consultation requirements may mean that the nearest relative is consulted in his or her capacity as the substantial part player (consultation with whom the patient does not have the right to block), but not in his or her capacity as the nearest relative.

## 15. The substantial part player

This person may or may not be the nearest relative. The Act requires this person to be someone who plays, or is likely to play, a substantial part in the after-care of the patient, but who is not professionally concerned with the after-care services. When the application is being prepared, it is the RMO who must make the judgment as to who this person should be; when the supervision is renewed it is the CRMO who judges who this person should be; and when the supervision ends it is the responsible after-care bodies who make this judgment.

A wide variety of persons may come in this category. The guidance uses the term informal carer, informal presumably denoting that the person is not paid for the work. It may be a relative, even the nearest relative, or it may be an advocate, a fellow resident in a hostel or home, a landlady or many others.

***Could this person be a professional?***

Yes, provided that the person is not professionally concerned with the after-care services being provided to the patient. Thus it may be a chaplain or nurse or another person who is not a professional member of the after-care team for the patient.

### *What role does this person have?*

This persons's statutory role is to be consulted, and informed on each of the occasions stated in the Act. However, there are no set statutory responsibilities placed upon this person. One would hope, however, that there would be good relationships between this person and the supervisor and the CRMO so that any untoward incidents or change in the patient's condition were notified to the supervisor and CRMO. The substantial part player should also have an important role in supporting the patient with regard to accepting the after-care services and complying with the requirements.

In addition, if the patient failed to take up the after-care services provided or to meet the requirements, then reliance would be placed upon this person to notify the supervisor or CRMO so that a review could be initiated.

### *What if there is no such person?*

The absence of such a person does not prevent the application, renewal etc going ahead, but it may make it more difficult for the supervisor to ensure compliance with the requirements and acceptance of the after-care services.

## 16. Patients sentenced to imprisonment or admitted for assessment under section 2

Section 25I makes the provisions shown in *Figure 32* in relation to a patient who is subject to after-care under supervision who is either detained in custody (under sentence or under remand) or detained in hospital in

**Figure 32: Patients under after-care under supervision who are imprisoned or placed under section (S.2. 25I(2))**

| | |
|---|---|
| **a.** | **the patient is not required to receive after-care services under S.117; or** |
| **b.** | **comply with requirements imposed under S.25D.** |

pursuance of an application for admission for assessment (ie section 2).

Extension of the period of after-care under supervision for such patients is shown in *Figure 33*.

**Figure 33: Extension of after-care under supervision time**

**S.25I(3)** **If the patient is detained for a period or periods of less that 6 months and if apart from this section he**

- **a. would have ceased to be subject to after-care under supervision or**
- **b. would cease to be during the period of 28 days of the section 2;**

**he shall be deemed not to have ceased, and shall not cease to be so subject until the end of the period of 28 days.**

**S.25I(4)** **Where the period of after-care under supervision is extended by virtue of this provision, any examination and report to be made and furnished for renewal under 25G may be made and furnished within the period as so extended.**

**S.25I(5)** **The renewal then commences on the day that he would have ceased to be so subject.**

The effect of the statutory provisions shown in *Figure 32* is to extend the period of validity of the after-care under supervision during the imprisonment (if imprisonment is for less than six months) or while the patient is under section 2.

## 17. Part III patients

**Figure 34: Part III patients**

- **None of the provisions of Part II in respect of after-care under supervision apply to the power of the High Courts to place the patient under restriction.**
- **Patients under an order or direction for admission or removal to hospital under Part III can be considered for after-care under supervision. (ie S.37, 47 and 48).**

Other amendments to the 1983 Act set out in Schedule 1

paragraph 6 of the 1995 Act apply the provisions of after-care under supervision to Part III patients who are placed under hospital orders without restrictions (ie section 37) and to those who are transferred under a hospital order from prison to hospital (ie sections 47 and 48), provided that they are not under restriction orders.

## 18. Offences

The 1995 Act creates new offences in relation to after-care under supervision by amending sections 126, 127 and 129 as shown below:

A. Section 126 offences relating to falsifying medical recommendations and reports is extended to 'other' recommendations and reports

B. A new 2A added to section 127 (*Figure 35*).

**Figure 35: Section 127(2A)**

- **It shall be an offence for any individual to ill-treat or wilfully to neglect a mentally disordered patient who is for the time being subject to after-care under supervision**

C. In section 129 (offence of obstruction) *or to give access to any person to a person so authorised* is added to the offence of obstruction in refusing to allow visiting, interviewing or examination.

## 19. Summary of HA responsibilities

The HA has the duties shown in *Figure 36*. All of them can be delegated except the duty of reviewing and modifying the after-care services under section 25E(1) and (3).

**Figure 36: Duties of the health authority in relation to supervision applications**

**S.117: with the LSSA to provide after-care services in conjunction with the voluntary sector;**

| | |
|---|---|
| **S.25A(6):** | **Receipt of application;** |
| **S.25A(7):** | **Consultation with LSSA on application;** |
| **S.25A(8):** | **Acceptance and notification of patient, etc;** |
| **S.25C(6):** | **Rectification of application and recommendations;** |
| **S.25D(1):** | **Imposition of requirements;** |
| **S.25E(1) and (3):*** | **Review and modification of requirements and after-care services;** |
| **S.25E(4):** | **Review for possible readmission;** |
| **S.25E(6):** | **Consultations about modifications;** |
| **S.25E(8):** | **Notification after modifications;** |
| **S.25E(11):** | **Notification after change of CRMO and/or supervisor;** |
| **S.25F(1):** | **Receipt of report of reclassification;** |
| **S.25F(4):** | **Notification following reclassification;** |
| **S.25G(3):** | **Receipt of report for renewal;** |
| **S.25G(8):** | **Notification following renewal;** |
| **S. 25H(6):** | **Notification following ending of after-care under supervision.** |

* The duties under S. 25E(1) and (3) cannot be delegated. All the other duties can be delegated and in most cases will be included in the NHS agreements between health authority and provider.

In practice, therefore, a service agreement between the HA as purchaser and a provider unit, usually an NHS trust, will place requirements upon the provider to carry out section 117 responsibilities and those in relation to after-care under supervision, as part of the mental health services contracted for. In the case of an NHS trust as provider, the trust will have the responsibility of carrying out all those functions listed in *Figure 36* with the exception of the duty to review and modify the after-care under supervision.

## 20. Summary of LSSA responsibilities.

These are shown in *Figure 37*.

**Figure 37: Duties of the Local Social Services Authority**

**S.117 with the HA to provide after-care services in conjunction with the voluntary sector;**
**S.25A(7) To be consulted by the HA on the after-care under supervision application;**
**S.25E(1) and (3) in association with the HA to review the after-care under supervision.**
**Other duties are laid down under the NHS and Community Care Act 1990 in respect of community care assessments, the preparation and revision of a community care plan and the inspection of premises for community care.**

The LSSA has the duty, with the HA to provide the after-care services under section 117, and where the HA has delegated this to another person or body then the LSSA can authorise the same person or body to perform all of the social services functions (paragraph 2(4) of the Regulations.) However, like the HA, it cannot delegate its responsibilities under the 1995 Act to review and modify the after-care under supervision (paragraph 2(5) of the Regulations.)

## 21. Documents: rectification (S.25C)

**Figure 38: Rectification of documents (S. 25C(6))**

| | |
|---|---|
| **a.** | **if, within 14 days beginning with the day on which the supervision application has been accepted;** |
| **b.** | **the application or any recommendation accompanying it is found in any respect incorrect or defective;** |
| **c.** | **the application or recommendation may within that period; and** |
| **d.** | **with the consent of the health authority which accepted the application;** |
| **e.** | **be amended by the person by whom it was made or given.** |

**The effect of the rectification is that it shall be deemed to have been made from the beginning.**

Where a supervision application appears to be duly made and to be accompanied by recommendations, then it can be acted upon without further proof of:

a. the signature or qualification of the person by whom the application or any recommendation was made or given; or

b. any matter of fact or opinion stated in the application or recommendation.

However, while the authorities can rely on the face value of the forms, if it subsequently becomes apparent that the documents were falsely completed then that could lead to the invalidation of the after-care under supervision.

For example, in the case of Re S[12], S, a mental patient, appealed against the dismissal of his application for a writ of habeas corpus following his admission to and detention in hospital under section 3 of the Mental Health Act 1983. He argued that the admission and detention were unlawful as the ASW had not completed the required application form correctly in accordance with section 11(4) of the 1983 Act, which provided that on making an application for treatment, an ASW had to consult with the nearest relative and could not proceed if that relative objected to the making of the application. In his case, the social worker had stated that she had consulted S's mother, believing her to be the nearest relative, when in fact the nearest relative was his father who objected to the application.

It was held that the detention was unlawful as the AWS's statement was false, since on the date of admission she knew that S's nearest relative was his father and that he objected to the admission. Any delegation of his role to the mother had to be in writing pursuant to regulation 14 of the Mental Health (Hospital, Guardianship, and Consent to Treatment) Regulations 1983, but no such authorisation had been given and therefore there was no authority to detain. S had not sought to overturn an administrative decision, but to show that the hospital lacked the jurisdiction to detain him. Therefore, an appropriate remedy was not by way of judicial review, as the local authority had proposed, but by a writ for *habeas corpus* as it was not for the court to rule that an apparently valid application was lawful when the statutory safeguards to protect mental patients had clearly not been followed. The matter would be adjourned to enable the HA to give reasons why S should continue to be detained.

Under the Regulations[1], statutory forms are to be used for after-care under supervision. These are shown below in *Table 4*

**Table 4: Statutory forms for after-care under supervision***

| | | |
|---|---|---|
| a. | Supervision application | Form 1S; |
| b. | Written recommendation of a registered medical practitioner | Form 2S; |
| c. | Written recommendation of approved social worker | Form 3S; |
| d. | Report for reclassification | Form 4S; |
| e. | Report for renewal | Form 5S; |
| f. | Record of renewal of after-care under supervision under part II | Form 5S; |
| g. | Direction for ending after-care under supervision | Form 6S. |

*(It should be noted that new forms for certain sections of the 1983 Act are required after 1 April 1996 following the Mental Health (Hospital, Guardianship and Consent to Treatment) (Amendment) Regulations 1996[2].

## 22. Supervision compared with guardianship

### How does supervision compare with guardianship?

*Figure 39* shows the difference between guardianship and after-care under supervision.

**Figure 39: Comparison of guardianship and after-care supervision**

| GUARDIANSHIP | AFTER-CARE UNDER SUPERVISION |
|---|---|
| Grounds: | Grounds: |
| a. specified form of mental disorder; | a. specified form of mental disorder; |
| b. necessary in the interests of the welfare of the patient or for the protection of other persons that he should be so received; | b. substantial risk of serious harm to: health of patient; safety of other persons; patient being seriously exploited; |
| | c. being under supervision is likely to help to secure that he receives the after-care services to be provided under S.117 |
| Need not be detained for treatment or even in hospital | Detained for treatment |
| 16 years and over | 16 years and over |

### Requirements under guardianship

These are:

a. the power to require the patient to reside at a place specified;

b. the power to require the patient to attend at places and times so specified for the purpose of medical treatment, occupation, education or training;

c. the power to require access to the patient to be given at any place where the patient is residing, to any RMP, ASW or other person so specified.

**Will the effect of the 1995 Act mean that guardianship will be used in preference to after-care under supervision?**

Since guardianship and after-care under supervision both require the presence of a specified form of mental disorder, neither can be used in respect of a patient who would satisfy the definition of mental disorder for the purposes of section 2 but does not have a specified form of mental disorder as defined (this applies to certain groups of patients with learning disabilities).

1. Guardianship can be imposed even though a patient has never been detained for treatment. After-care under supervision can only be imposed on those who are at present detained for treatment.
2. There are considerable consultation provisions for after-care under supervision which are not statutorily required for guardianship (although good practice would include them).
3. The main advantage of after-care under supervision is the ability to convey the patient to the place specified for medical treatment, education, training etc. However, this may not in practice be found to be of great value.
4. For both guardianship and after-care under supervision, the patient can be returned to the specified place.
5. There is no specified CRMO for a patient under guardianship, but in practice there would be a doctor responsible for caring for the patient in the community.
6. The GP would not necessarily be section 12 approved, wheras the CRMO must be section 12 approved.

In summary, guardianship covers most of the facets of after-care under supervision with less paperwork, with the ASW as applicant and with a named guardian. The additional powers for conveying a patient placed under after-care under super- vision may prove of little value. In addition, even though it is not a statutory requirement it would be good practice to ensure that a patient subject to guardianship was under the clinical management of a section 12 approved doctor. Should the patient fail to comply with a requirement listed under the guardianship order, a review of the patient would be initiated and this could lead to a readmission under section to hospital (exactly as for after-care under supervision, but without the same statutory requirement).

## 23. Section 117 after-care services

### Amendments to section 117

***Schedule 1 paragraph 15(2) section 117(1)*** This comes into effect when the patient ceases to be detained and (*whether or not immediately after so ceasing*), leaves hospital. Section 117(1) now reads as shown in *Figure 40*.

**Figure 40: Section 117(1)**

**This section applies to persons who are detained under section 3 above, or admitted to hospital in pursuance of a hospital order under S.37 above, or transferred to a hospital in pursuance of a transfer direction made under S.47 or 48 above, and then cease to be detained and (whether or not immediately after so ceasing) leave hospital.**

***Schedule 1 paragraph 15(3)*** The duty of the HA and the LSSA continues 'until such time as the health authority and the local social services are satisfied that the person concerned is no longer in need of such services, *but they shall not be so satisfied in the case of a patient who is subject to* *after-care under supervision at any time while he remains so subject'* (words in italic added by Schedule 1 paragraph 15(3).

***Schedule 1 paragraph 15(4) section 117(2A)*** New subsection added by Schedule 1 is shown in *Figure 41*.

**Figure 41: Section 117(2A)**

**It shall be the duty of the Health Authority to secure that at all times while a patient is subject to after-care under supervision:**

**a. a person who is a registered medical practitioner approved for the purposes of section 12 above by the Secretary of State as having special experience in the diagnosis or treatment of mental disorder is in charge of the medical treatment provided for the patient as part of the after-care services provided for him under the section; and**

**b. a person professionally concerned with any of the after-care services so provided is supervising him with a view to securing that he receives the after-care services so provided.**

**2B Section 32 (regulations) shall apply for the purposes of S.117 as it applies for the purposes of Part II of this Act.**

## 24. Movement from Scotland (S.25J)

A supervision application may be made in respect of a patient who is subject to a community care order under the Mental Health (Scotland) Act 1984 and who intends to leave Scotland in order to reside in England and Wales (S.25J(1)). Separate provisions for Scotland and the establishment of a community care order are set out in the 1995 Act but are not further discussed in this booklet.

## 25. Movement within England and Wales

Where a patient subject to after-care under supervision wishes to move from one area to another within England

Wales, it would be necessary for the provisions for changing the CRMO and the supervisor to be implemented. In addition, the HA would have to agree to the change of the specified place of residence. Cooperation between the appropriate LSSAs and the NHS trusts would be essential.

## 26. Miscellaneous provisions

### Power to make regulations

The Secretary of State has the power to modify the provisions for after-care under supervision and section 117 by regulations (S.25J(2)).

## 27. Policies

Policies that authorities will find it of value to draft include:

1. Who can be the supervisor?
2. Procedure for making applications, including ensuring that an application is made before the patient is taken off section.
3. Section 117 meeting and preparation for after-care under supervision.
4. Communication between the managers and the professionals that the application has been accepted.
5. Contacting the voluntary services.
6. Contact with employment and housing agencies.
7. Confidentiality over patient being on the list of those on after-care under supervision: could supervisor ask employer/centre manager/trainer to notify her or him if the patient fails to come to work/centre etc?

Inferences which may be made from a request to 'let me know if he does not attend'.

8. Application of enforcement of requirements.
9. Procedure for getting access to patient.
10. When to discharge from after-care under supervision.
11. Procedures when there are different trusts/HAs/ social service departments and cross-boundary anomalies, ie patient may be subject to one NHS trust but live in a catchment area of an LSSA outside the NHS trust area.
12. Who provides information to patient and how, and what documentation should be completed?
13. Links with ambulance and police.
14. Monitoring and review of the implementation of the provisions for after-care under supervision.

# Part II

# Absence without leave

## Section 2 of 1995 Act Amendments to sections 18 and 21 of Mental Health Act 1983

Section 18 relates to the return of a patient liable to be detained who is absent without leave, or who has been given leave of absence but has failed to return when recalled, or whose leave of absence has expired. There was under the 1983 Act prior to the amendment a rule that if a patient absent without leave was absent for 28 days or more then the section expired. Section 21 permits the length of the section to be extended to permit the responsible medical offier to renew the period of detention. Section 18 is shown with the changes brought about by the 1995 Act in *Figure 42* and the new section 21 in *Figures 43, 44* and *45*.

**Figure 42: Section 18**

**1. Where a patient who is liable to be detained in hospital:**

- **a. absents himself without leave granted under S.17;**
- **b. fails to return at the end of S.17 leave or on recall from S.17 leave;**
- **c. absents himself from any place where he is required to reside without permission,**

**he may subject to the provisions of this section, be taken into custody, and returned to the hospital or place by any approved social worker, by any officer on the staff of the hospital or by any person authorised in writing by the managers of the hospital.**

| Figure 42: Section 18 (contd) | |
|---|---|
| **2.** | **(see below)** |
| **3.** | **A patient under guardianship who absents himself without leave of the guardian from the place where he is required to reside may be taken into custody and returned to that place by any officer on the staff of a local social services authority, by any constable, or by any person authorised in writing by the guardian or local social services authority.** |
| **4.** | **(see *Figure 43* below)** |
| **5.** | **A patient cannot be returned under this section if he is under section 2(4), or 4(4), or 5(2), or 5(4) and that period of detention has expired.** |

Section 18(2) covers the situation where the place referred to in paragraph c of section 18(1) is a different hospital from the one in which the patient is for the time being liable to be detained. In such a situation, references to the managers and staff of the hospital refer to the first-mentioned hospital.

**Figure 43: New section 18(4)**

**S.18(4): A patient shall not be taken into custody under this section after the later of:**

**a. the end of the period of six months beginning with the first day of his absence without leave; and**

**b. the end of the period for which (apart from section 21 below) he is liable to be detained or subject to guardianship;**

**and, in determining for the purposes of paragraph (b) above or any other provision of this Act whether a person is or has been absent without leave is at any time liable to be detained or subject to guardianship, a report furnished under section 20 or 21B below before the first day of his absence without leave shall not be taken to have renewed the authority for his detention or guardianship unless the period of renewal began before that day (ie the 28-day rule for returning the patient absent without leave is repealed.)**

The basic principles which emerge from section 18 as revised are:

1. Patients detained under section 2(4), 4(4), or 5(2), or 5(4) cannot be taken into custody, once the period of their detention under that section has expired (S.18(5)).
2. Patients under a restriction order or direction can be taken into custody under section 18(1) and no time limits apply (Schedule 1 part II, paragraph 4 of the 1983 Act).
3. Patients liable to be detained for treatment can be taken into custody while the section is still valid, or up to six months from the first day of their leave, whichever is the later (S.18(4)).
4. Section 21 enables the period of detention to be extended by up to a week in certain cases and draws a distinction between patients who have been absent without leave for 28 days or less and those absent without leave for longer than 28 days.

## Section 21

The original section is repealed and a new section is introduced by section 2(2) of the 1995 Act. The new section is complex and is shown in Figures 44–49.

- *Figure 44* covers the provision to extend the period of detention by up to a week in certain cases
- *Figure 45* covers the situation which applies if the absence without leave has been 28 days or less
- *Figure 46* covers the situation which applies if the absence without leave has been more than 28 days
- *Figure 47* covers the implications of the report provided on patients who are absent without leave for more than 28 days

- *Figure 48* covers the reclassification of the patient's form of mental disorder
- *Figure 49* covers definitions given for section 21B

**Figure 44: Section 21 as amended**

1. **Where a patient is absent without leave:**
   a. **on the day on which (apart from this section) he would cease to be liable to be detained or subject to guardianship; or**
   b. **within the period of one week ending with that day, he shall not cease to be so liable or subject until the relevant time.**
2. **Relevant time means:**
   a. **where the patient is taken into custody under section 18 above, is the end of the period or one week beginning with the day on which he is returned to the hospital or place where he ought to be;**
   b. **where the patient himself returns to the hospital or place where he ought to be within the period during which he can be taken into custody under section 18, is the end of the period beginning with the day on which he so returns himself; and**
   c. **otherwise, is the end of the period during which he can be taken into custody under section 18 above**

The significance of section 21(1) can be seen from the following example:

> ***Patient A****, who was detained under section 3 which was due to expire on 31 October 1996, left the hospital without leave of absence on 3 September 1996. Under section 18(4) (see Figure 43) he could be returned for up to six months from 3 September 1996. If he is retaken on 20 November 1996, this is outside the original period of detention and under section 21(2)(a) the period of detention is the end of one week beginning with the 20 November 1996. This will give the RMO time to*

*consider whether the patient's continued detention is necessary and to arrange for the period of detention to be renewed.*

### *Section 21 and patients who return from absence without leave within or after 28 days.*

| Figure 45: Patients absent without leave for 28 days or less (S.21A, simplified) | |
|---|---|
| 1. | Where the patient returns or is returned no later than 28 days beginning with his first day of absence without leave; |
| 2. | and the period for which he is liable to be detained is extended by S.21(1), any examination and report to be made under S.20 (for renewal) may be made and furnished during the period as so extended. |
| 3. | The renewal then takes effect from that day. |

*Figure 45* sets out the procedure to be followed for patients who are absent without leave for 28 days or less and makes provision for the renewal of their period of detention to be made, if necessary.

### *Patients who are absent without leave for longer than 28 days*

Special provisions are required to be followed for these patients. These are set out in *Figures* 46 and *47*. The RMO must examine the patient and if appropriate furnish a report on the necessity for the continued detention of the patient. Failure to furnish the report within one week means that the patient ceases to be liable to be detained (S.21B(4))

**Figure 46: Patients absent without leave for more than 28 days (S.21B)**

**21B(1).** Where the patient returns or is returned no later than 28 days beginning with his first day of absence without leave;

**21B(2).** It shall be the duty of the appropriate medical officer, within the period of one week beginning with the day on which the patient is returned or returns to the hospital or the place where he ought to be:

- a. to examine; and
- b. if it appears to him that the relevant conditions are satisfied, to furnish to the appropriate body a report to that effect in the prescribed form; and where such a report is furnished in respect of the patient the appropriate body shall cause him to be informed.

**21B(3).** Before furnishing the report the RMO must (where the patient is liable to be detained as opposed to guardianship), consult:

- a. one or more other persons who have been professionally concerned with the patient's medical treatment; and
- b. an approved social worker.

**Figure 47: Significance of report under section 21B (simplified)**

**21B(4).** Where a patient would have been liable to be detained, he shall cease to be so liable unless a report is furnished under S.21B(2);

**21B(5).** Where a patient would have ceased to be so liable, furnishing the report under S.21B(2) shall renew the authority for his detention or guardianship.

**21B(6).** Where the authority for the detention or guardianship is renewed by virtue of S.21B(5):

- a. the renewal shall take effect as from the day on which (apart from S.21) the authority would have expired; and
- b. if (apart from this paragraph) the renewed authority would expire on or before the day on which the report is furnished, the report shall further renew the authority, as from the day on which it would expire, for the period prescribed in that case by S.20(2) above.

**Figure 47: Significance of report under 21B (simplified)(contd)**

**21B(7).** **Where the authority for the detention or guardianship of the patient would expire within the period of two months beginning with the day on which a report is duly furnished in respect of him under subsection (2) above, the report shall, if it so provides, have effect also as a report duly furnished under S.20(3) or (6) above; and the reference in this subsection to authority includes any authority renewed under subsection (5) above by the report.**

Section 21B(7) provides that if the report furnished under 21B(2) is within two months of the patient's detention coming to an end, then it can count as a renewal report under section 20.

Provisions are made for the reclassification of the form of mental disorder from which the patient suffers and are shown in *Figure 48*.

**Figure 48: Reclassification of mental disorder under section 21B**

**21B(8).** **Where the form of mental disorder specified in a report furnished under S.21B(2) is different from that specified in the application, (and the report does not have the effect of a renewal under S.20), the application shall have effect as if the new form of disorder was specified in it.**

**21B(9).** **The RMO does not then have to comply with S.16 (reclassification of mental disorder).**

Definitions for the section are given in section 21B(10) (see *Figure 49*).

**Figure 49: Definitions for section 21B**

**21B(10).Appropriate medical officer — the same meaning as in S.16(5)**

**Appropriate body: patient liable to be detained = managers of hospital; or**

**patient subject to guardianship = local social services authority and relevant conditions:**

**a. patient liable to be detained — conditions under S.20(4)**

**b. patient subject to guardianship — conditions under S.20(7)**

# Part III

# Leave of absence under section 17

## Section 3 of 1995 Act: Amendments to section 17

### Section 17 changes

Under section 17 the responsible medical officer can give leave of absence to a patient detained under the Act (who is not under a restriction direction or order) on such terms as he or she considers necessary in the interests of the patient or for the protection of other persons. Under the 1983 Mental Health Act, leave could however only be given up to a maximum of six months. This was because under section 17(5) any patient give section 17 leave shall cease to be liable to be detained at the expiration of six months beginning with the first day of his or her absence on leave, unless he or she is either returned to the hospital or transferred, or he or she is absent without leave at the end of six months. Section 3 of the Mental Health (Patients in the Community) Act 1995 amended this provision. The law is now:

A patient on section 17 leave shall cease to be liable to be recalled after he or she has ceased to be liable to be detained ie:

1. **The section 17 leave can last for as long as the section under which the patient is detained (in the case of patients who are on their second section 3 renewal up to twelve months)**
2. **They can be recalled as long as the section lasts.**

The amendments to section 17 apply to patients who have been given leave before the section actually comes into force, ie 1 April 1996.

# Part IV

# Conclusions

## Building Bridges[13]

In February 1996 the Department of Health published *Building Bridges*, a guide to arrangements for inter-agency working for the care and protection of severely mentally ill people, which formed part of its response to the Christopher Clunis Inquiry. It is intended as a resource document for health and social care purchasers and providers. Its main contents are shown in *Figure 50*.

**Figure 50: Building Bridges: summary of contents**

| | |
|---|---|
| 1. | Introduction and overview |
| 2. | Roles of agencies involved in caring for mentally ill people |
| 3. | Working of the Care Programme Approach |
| 4. | Supervision registers and information systems |
| 5. | If things go wrong: audits and inquiries |
| 6. | Continuing education and training |
| Appendices | |
| | Relationships between the Care Programme Approach and other key processes and provisions |
| | Discharged patients to whom legal requirements apply |
| | Checklists for action |
| | Availability of accommodation |
| | Integrating the Care Programme Approach and Care Management |
| | NHS Information and Technology Strategy documents |

Properly resourced, a mental health strategy based upon *Building Bridges* and fully implemented should provide a quality service for mentally disturbed patients.

## The future

It will be some time before the full effects of the Mental Health (Patients in the Community) Act 1995 are seen and it is established whether after-care under supervision provides the net which prevents long-term, chronically sick, seriously mentally disturbed patients becoming lost to the system. It may be, as some have suggested, that the problem is simply one of resources, and that if there were the staff, the hostel places, the day centre places etc, further compulsion of such patients in the community would not be required. It also remains to be seen whether fears about the breakdown of the therapeutic relationship between professional and patient will be exacerbated by after-care under supervision. It will be interesting to note the frequency with which such an order is used, and whether certain districts make greater use of it than others, and if so, the reasons for the discrepancy. It will also be interesting to note the effects of the new legislation on the use of guardianship orders.

It will also become apparent how enthusiastic the Government is in pursuing the review of the Mental Health Act 1983 and the nature of the changes which are made and the effects of any consultation which must precede such a revision. In September 1996 it was announced, following publicity of the actions of recently discharged patients, that legislation would be introduced to remove the powers of the hospital managers to discharge detained patients. Similar proposals may be developed as *ad hoc* reactions to specific situations.

What is certain is that there will be continual media interest in the extent to which community care is seen to be failing, as every criminal action and act of self-harm by former mental hospital patients is highlighted and exposed. It is essential that all health and social services professionals caring for those with mental disabilities and illness should be prepared to take their full part in the consultation which precedes any changes to the existing law.

# References


1. *The Mental Health (After-care under Supervision) Regulations* 1996. Statutory Instrument 1996, No 294
2. *The Mental Health (Hospital, Guardianship and Consent to Treatment (Amendment) Regulations* 1996. Statutory Instrument 1996, No 540
3. Department of Health Welsh Office (1996) *Guidance on Supervised Discharge (After-care under Supervision) and Related Provisions*. Supplement to the Code of Practice, published August 1993 pursuant to Section 118 of the Mental Health Act 1983
4. Department of Health (1993) Press announcement, 12 August. *Legislation planned to provide for supervised discharge: ten-point plan for developing successful and safe community care*. DoH, London
5. Ritchie J, Dick D, Lingham R (1994) *The Report of the Inquiry into the Care and Treatment of Christopher Clunis*. HMSO, London
6. Department of Health (1994) NHS Management Executive HSG(94) 27. *Guidance on the Discharge of Mentally Disordered People and their Continuing Care in the Community*. DoH, London
7. Taken from the Report of the Panel of Inquiry Appointed to Investigate the Case of Kim Kirkman. West Midlands Regional Health Authority
8. W v L (1974) Q B, 711
9. Hoggett B (1996) *Mental Health Law*. Sweet and Maxwell, London

10. ex parte Fox [1993] 3 All ER 170. R v Ealing District Health Authority

11. *The Times* (1995) Letter dated 16 March from MIND, BASW, Survivors Speak Out, Law Society, Mental Health Foundation, CPN Association, Liberty

12. Re SC (Mental Patient: *Habeas Corpus*) [1996] 1FLR 548

13. Department of Health (1996) *The Health of the Nation: Building Bridges: A Guide to Arrangements for Inter-agency Working for the Care and Protection of Severely Mentally Ill People*. DoH, London

# Further reading

Audit Commission (1994) *Finding a Place: A Review of Mental Health Service for Adults*. HMSO, London

Blom-Cooper L *et al* (1992) *Report of Inquiry into Ashworth Hospital*

Blom-Cooper L, Holly H, Murphy E (1996) *The Falling Shadow: One Patient's Mental Health Care 1978–1993. Report on Inquiry into the Incident at the Edith Morgan Centre Torbay on 1 September 1993*. Duckworth, London

Blom-Cooper L *et al* (1996) *The Case of Jason Mitchell: Report of the Independent Panel of Inquiry*. Duckworth, London

Bluglass R (1992) *Guide to the Mental Health Act*. Churchill Livingstone, Edinburgh

Brazier M (1992) *Medicine Patients and the Law*. Penguin, Harmondsworth

Department of Health (1989) *Caring for People*. HMSO, London

Department of Health (1990) *The Care Programme Approach* HC(90) 23. HMSO, London

Department of Health (1993) *Code of Practice on the Mental Health Act 1983*, 2nd edn. Department of Health Welsh Office

Dimond BC (1993) *Patients Rights, Responsibilities and the Nurse*, Central Health Studies series. Quay Publishing, Lancaster

Dimond BC (1995) *Legal Aspects of Nursing*, 2nd edn. Prentice Hall, Hemel Hempstead

Dimond BC, Barker F (1996) *Mental Health Law for Nurses*. Blackwell Scientific, Oxford

Dimond B (1997) *Legal Aspects of Care in the Community.* Macmillans, London

Finch J (1994) *Speller's Law Relating to Hospitals*, 17th edn. Chapman and Hall Medical, London

Gann R (1993) *The NHS A to Z: The Help for Health Trust*, 2nd edn. The Help for Health Trust, London

Gostin L, Oglethorpe L (1992) *Mental Health Tribunal Procedures,* 2nd edn. Longman, Harlow

Ham C (1991 *The New National Health Service*. NAHAT, London

Hoggett B (1996) *Mental Health Law*. Sweet and Maxwell, London

Hunt G, Wainwright P, eds (1994) *Expanding the Role of the Nurse*. Blackwell Scientific, Oxford

Jones R (1994) *Mental Health Act Manual*, 4th edn. Sweet and Maxwell, London

Law Commission (1991 and 1993) *Reports on the Incapacitated Adult: Decision Making No 119 (1991); Nos 128, 129, and 130 (1993)*. HMSO, London

Law Commission (1995) *Report on Mental Incapacity No 231.* HMSO, London

Lingham R *et al* (1996) *Report of the Inquiry into the Treatment and Care of Raymond Sinclair.* West Kent Health Authority

Peay J (1996) *Inquiries After Homicide*. Duckworth, London

Pyne RH (1991) *Professional Discipline in Nursing, Midwifery and Health Visiting,* 2nd edn. Blackwell Scientific, Oxford

Ritchie J, Dick D, Lingham R (1994) *The Report of the Inquiry into the Care and Treatment of Christopher Clunis*. HMSO, London

Rowson R (1990) *An Introduction to Ethics for Nurses*. Scutari, Harrow

Rumbold G (1993) *Ethics in Nursing Practice,* 2nd edn. Baillière Tindall, London

Young AP (1989) *Legal Problems in Nursing Practice*. Harper and Rowe, London

Young AP (1994) *Law and Professional Conduct in Nursing,* 2nd edn. Scutari, Harrow

Reference should also be made to the publications published by MIND and MENCAP (see addresses)

# Useful Addresses

Alzheimer's Disease Society, Gordon House, 10 Greencoat Place, London SW1P 1PH; *Tel: 0171 306 0606*

Association of Directors of Social Services, Social Services Dept, North Yorkshire CC, County Hall, Northallerton, N Yorks DL7 8DD; *Tel: 01609 770661; Fax: 01609 773158*

Association of Mental Health Act Administrators, c/o Mental Health Act Administrator, The Maudsley Hospital, Denmark Hill, London SE5 8AZ; *Tel: 0171 703 6333*

British Association of Social Workers, 16 Kent Street, Birmingham B5 6RD; *Tel: 0121 622 3911; Fax: 0121 622 4860*

British Institute of Learning Disabilities (BILD), Wolverhampton Road, Kidderminster, Worcs DY10 3PP; *Tel: 01562 850251; Fax: 01562 851970*

Counsel and Care for the Elderly, Twyman House, 16 Bonny Street, London NW1 9PG; *Tel: 0171 485 1550*

English National Board, Victory House, 170 Tottenham Court Road, London W1P 0HA; *Tel: 0171 388 3131; Fax: 0171 383 4031*

Good Practices in Mental Health, 380–384 Harrow Road, London W9 2HU; *Tel: 0171 289 2034/3060*

Headway (National Head Injuries Association), 7 King Edward Court, King Edward Street, Nottingham NG1 1EW; *Tel: 0115 924 0800*

Health Service Commissioner (The Ombudsman)(England), Church House, Great Smith Street, London SW1P 3BW; *Tel: 0171 276 2035*

Health Service Commissioner (The Ombudsman)(Wales), 4th Floor, Pearl Assurance House, Cardiff CF1 3AG; *Tel: 01222 394621*

MENCAP see Royal Society of Mentally Handicapped Children and Adults

Mental Health After-Care Association, 25 Bedford Square, London WC1B 3HW; *Tel: 0171 436 6194*

Mental Health Act Commission, Maid Marian House, 56 Hounds Gate, Nottingham NG1 6BG; *Tel: 0115 950 4040; Fax: 0115 950 5998*

Mental Health Foundation, 37 Mortimer Street, London W1N 7RJ; *Tel: 0171 580 0145; Fax: 0171 631 3868*

Mental Health Review Tribunals:

Liverpool 3rd Floor, Cressington House, 249 St Mary's Road, Garston, Liverpool L19 0NF; *Tel: 0151 494 0095*

London (North), Spur 3 Block 1, Government Buildings, Honeypot Lane, Stanmore, Middlesex HA7 1AY; *Tel: 0171 972 3738*

London (South), Block 3 Crown Offices, Kingston Bypass Road, Surbiton, Surrey KT6 5QN; *Tel: 0181 398 4166*

Nottingham, Spur A Block 5, Government Buildings, Chalfont Drive, Western Boulevard, Nottingham NG8 3RZ; *Tel: 0115 929 4222*

Wales, 1st Floor, New Crown Buildings, Cathays Park, Cardiff CF1 3NQ; *Tel: 01222 823036*

MIND National Association for Mental Health, Granta House, 15–19 Broadway, Stratford, London E15 4BQ; *Tel: 0181 519 2122*

National Association of Crossroads Caring for Carers, 10 Regents Place, Rugby; *Tel: 01778 573653*

National Association for Voluntary Hostels, Fulham Palace, Bishops Avenue, London SW6 6EA; *Tel: 0171 731 4205*

National Autistic Society, 276 Willesden Lane, London NW2 5RB; *Tel: 0181 451 1114*

National Board for Nursing, Midwifery and Health Visiting for Northern Ireland, 79 Chichester Street, Belfast BT1 4JE; *Tel: 01232 238152*

National Council of Voluntary Organisations, Regents Wharf, 8 All Saint's Street, London N1 9RL; Tel 0171 713 6161

National Schizophrenia Fellowship, 28 Castle Street, Kingston upon Thames, Surrey KT1 1SS; *Tel: 0181 547 3937; Fax: 0181 574 3862*

Registered Nursing Homes, Calthorpe House, Hagley Road, Edgbaston, Birmingham B16 8QY; *Tel: 0121 454 2511; Fax: 0121 454 0932*

Richmond Fellowship for Community Mental Health, 8 Addison Road, London W14 8DL; *Tel: 0171 603 6373; Fax: 0171 602 8652*

Royal Society for Mentally Handicapped Children and Adults (MENCAP), MENCAP National Centre, 123 Golden Lane, London EC1Y 0RT; *Tel: 0171 454 0454; Fax: 0171 608 3254*

Scottish National Board for Nursing Midwifery and Health Visiting, 22 Queen Street, Edinburgh EH2 1NT; *Tel: 0131 226 7371*

United Kingdom Central Council for Nursing Midwifery and Health Visiting, 23 Portland Place, London W1A 1BA; *Tel: 0171 637 7181; Fax: 0171 436 2924*

Welsh National Board forNursing Midwifery and Health Visiting, Floor 13, Pearl Assurance House, Greyfriars Road, Cardiff CF1 3AG; *Tel: 01222 395535; Fax: 01222 229366*

# Index